DIFFICULT LEVEL

MATCHING CHINESE CHARACTERS AND PINYIN

把汉字和拼音连起来

MANDARIN CHINESE PINYIN TEST SERIES

测试你的拼音知识

PART 16

Simplified Mandarin Chinese Characters with Pinyin and English, Mind Games, Test Your Knowledge of Pinyin with Multiple Answer Choice Puzzle Questions, Fast Reading & Vocabulary, Answers Included, Easy Lessons for Beginners, HSK All Levels

DENG YIXIN 邓艺心

ACKNOWLEDGEMENT

I would like to thank everyone who helped me complete this book, including my teachers, family members, friends, colleagues.

谢谢

Deng Yixin

邓艺心

INTRODUCTION

Chinese language and culture are a huge concept. In order to understand and appreciate Mandarin Chinese, we need to understand the language. Learning Chinese character is a very important part of learning the language. And, yes, learning pinyin is a must!

Welcome to **Connecting Chinese Characters and Pinyin Test Series**. Now you can test the knowledge of your Chinese pinyin (测试你的拼音知识). In these books and lessons therein, you will learn recognizing pinyin of the simplified Chinese characters. The books contain hundreds of character-pinyin matching **puzzles** (questions). For each question, there are Chinese characters in the left column and pinyin in the right column. You need to guess the correct pinyin of the given characters (把汉字和拼音连起来). The **English** meanings of the Chinese characters has been included a quick reference. The answers of all the question are provided at the end of the book.

CONTENTS

CHAPTER 1: QUESTIONS (1-30)

#1.

A. 窗 — 1. Zhù (Live)

B. 住 — 2. Kān (May)

C. 谤 — 3. Chuāng (Window)

D. 汾 — 4. Guì (Expensive)

E. 堪 — 5. Bàng (Slander)

F. 贵 — 6. Fén (The name of a river in Shanxi Province)

#2.

A. 龈 — 1. Shāo (A little)

B. 鹈 — 2. Qíng (Feeling)

C. 情 — 3. Tí (Pelican)

D. 粟 — 4. Yín (Gum)

E. 稍 — 5. Jiē (All)

F. 皆 — 6. Sù ()

#3.

A. 贵 — 1. Wèi (Rising)

B. 旮 — 2. Ruò (Weak)

C. 弱 | 3. Guì (Expensive)

D. 𠩺 | 4. Kè (Carve)

E. 刻 | 5. Gā (Corner)

F. 霨 | 6. Huī (Clash)

#4.

A. 寂 | 1. Jì (Lonely)

B. 粤 | 2. Bèi (Exhausted)

C. 惫 | 3. Yǎo (Far and deep)

D. 巷 | 4. Hàng (Tunnel)

E. 椅 | 5. Yuè (Another name for Guangdong Province)

F. 窅 | 6. Yǐ (Chair)

#5.

A. 赝 | 1. Qǔ (Bad teeth)

B. 轱 | 2. Yàn (Counterfeit)

C. 龋 | 3. Lì (Lynx)

D. 猁 | 4. Gū (Vehicle)

E. 骓 | 5. Qín (A surname)

F. 覃 | 6. Zhuī (Brindle)

#6.

A. 那 — 1. Suí (The Sui Dynasty)

B. 痕 — 2. Hén (Mark)

C. 搴 — 3. Wū (What)

D. 於 — 4. Qiān (Wrest away by hand)

E. 搁 — 5. Nè (That)

F. 隋 — 6. Gé (Bear)

#7.

A. 胀 — 1. Jiù (Old)

B. 竖 — 2. Xù (To raise (domestic animal))

C. 畜 — 3. Zhàng (Expand)

D. 正 — 4. Qián (Pious)

E. 旧 — 5. Zhēng (The first moon)

F. 虔 — 6. Shù (Vertical)

#8.

A. 豕 — 1. Shǎng (Falling-rising tone)

B. 戚 — 2. Bié (Change)

C. 上 — 3. Chóng (Repeat)

D. 重 — 4. Jiè (Joint of bones)

E. 豕

F. 戚

5. Shǐ (Pig)

6. Qī (Relative)

#9.

A. 罢

B. 稚

C. 开

D. 糯

E. 饮

F. 犀

1. Bà (Stop)

2. Kāi (Open)

3. Zhì (Young)

4. Nuò (Glutinous (cereal))

5. Xī (Rhinoceros)

6. Yǐn (Drink)

#10.

A. 硅

B. 校

C. 翕

D. 索

E. 熏

F. 赃

1. Suǒ (A large rope)

2. Xūn (Smoke)

3. Zāng (Stolen)

4. Jiào (Check)

5. Xī (Amiable and compliant)

6. Guī (Silicon)

#11.

A. 驳

1. Quán (Complete)

B. 浍　　2. Mèi (Sister)

C. 全　　3. Gāng (A surname)

D. 江　　4. Duì (Answer)

E. 妹　　5. Bó (Refute)

F. 对　　6. Huì (Ditch in the fields)

#12.

A. 盟　　1. Méng (Alliance)

B. 斤　　2. Chuǎi (Surmise)

C. 凷　　3. Kuài (Dirt clod)

D. 勼　　4. Yíng (Entangle)

E. 揣　　5. Jiū (Gather)

F. 萦　　6. Jīn (Jin, a unit of weight (0.5Kg))

#13.

A. 倚　　1. Dí (Bamboo flute)

B. 殠　　2. Chòu (Stink)

C. 笛　　3. Zǐ (To cultivate the soil (on plant roots))

D. 称　　4. Yǐ (Lean on or against)

E. 戎　　5. Chèn (Fit)

F. 耔　　6. Róng (Army)

#14.

A. 盛 | 1. Kān (Suppress)
B. 篾 | 2. Miè (Thin bamboo strip)
C. 戡 | 3. Guāi (Obedient)
D. 浆 | 4. Jiàng (Thick)
E. 凇 | 5. Shèng (Flourishing)
F. 乖 | 6. Sōng (Rime)

#15.

A. 袜 | 1. Yíng (Glimmering)
B. 荧 | 2. Zuàn (Deceive)
C. 赚 | 3. Wà (Hose)
D. 酸 | 4. Wò (Turn)
E. 斡 | 5. Suān (Acid)
F. 邪 | 6. Xié (Evil)

#16.

A. 伦 | 1. Xī (Rare)
B. 功 | 2. Yǐn (Hide)
C. 亨 | 3. Lún (Order)

D. 隐 — 4. Hēng (Prosperous)

E. 稀 — 5. Ài (Love)

F. 爱 — 6. Gōng (Exploit)

#17.

A. 洁 — 1. Zhòu (Day)

B. 咫 — 2. Quán (Spring)

C. 贫 — 3. Pín (Poor)

D. 泉 — 4. Jié (Clean)

E. 注 — 5. Zhǐ (An ancient measure of length, equal to 8 cun)

F. 昼 — 6. Zhù (Pour)

#18.

A. 糊 — 1. Kē (A kind of scarf in ancient times)

B. 殃 — 2. Yāng (Calamity)

C. 奋 — 3. Xián (Bowstring)

D. 匼 — 4. Jǐng (Surname)

E. 井 — 5. Fèn (Strenuous)

F. 弦 — 6. Hù (Paste)

#19.

A. 扃

B. 黦

C. 周

D. 粟

E. 翊

F. 襁

1. Qiǎng (Swaddling clothes)

2. Yì (Assist)

3. Yuè (Yellowish-black)

4. Sù ()

5. Zhōu (Circumference)

6. Jiōng (A bolt or hook for fastening a door from outside)

#20.

A. �

B. 宁

C. 当

D. 栈

E. 辜

F. 秋

1. Qiū (Autumn)

2. Xù (A surname)

3. Zhàn (Shed)

4. Dàng (Proper)

5. Gū (Crime)

6. Níng (Peaceful)

#21.

A. 悫

B. 汭

C. 磊

D. 旬

E. 聿

1. Ruì (The confluence of streams)

2. Què (Sincere)

3. Lěi (Of heap of stone)

4. Xún (A period of ten days)

5. Yù (Then)

F. 裕 6. Yù (Abundant)

#22.

A. 驿 1. Gòng (Offerings)

B. 粗 2. Yì (Glistening)

C. 硕 3. Yì (Station)

D. 供 4. Háo (Raccoon dog)

E. 熠 5. Shuò (Large)

F. 貉 6. Cū (Wide)

#23.

A. 曝 1. Pù (Expose)

B. 冻 2. Tián (Field)

C. 揣 3. Bà (Pa)

D. 田 4. Chuāi (Hide things in one's clothes)

E. 爸 5. Shì (Type)

F. 式 6. Dòng (Freeze)

#24.

A. 浆 1. Jiāng (Thick liquid)

B. 聿 2. Yīn (Gray horse)

C. 凄 3. Mù (Boat)

D. 驷 4. Liè (Hunt)

E. 猎 5. Qī (Chilly)

F. 艒 6. Yù (Then)

#25.

A. 媚 1. Hū (Plaster)

B. 驿 2. Mèi (Flatter)

C. 浒 3. Hǔ (Waterside)

D. 糊 4. Qué (Be lame)

E. 饮 5. Yì (Station)

F. 瘸 6. Yìn (Give water to drink)

#26.

A. 酷 1. Lóng (Deaf)

B. 京 2. Jīng (The capital of a country)

C. 聋 3. Jiàn (Warship)

D. 皱 4. Zhòu (Crease)

E. 膀 5. Bàng (Row)

F. 舰 6. Kù (Cruel)

#27.

A. 了 1. Tū (Dash forward)

B. 齑 2. Jī (Fine)

C. 欧 3. Máng (Chinese silver grass)

D. 邙 4. Le (Particle of completed action)

E. 突 5. Máng (The name of the mountain, in Henan Province, China)

F. 芒 6. Ōu (Short for Europe)

#28.

A. 沉 1. Chén (Sink)

B. 甓 2. Sī (This)

C. 宥 3. Líng (Imperial tomb)

D. 属 4. Pì (Brick)

E. 陵 5. Yòu (Pardon)

F. 斯 6. Zhǔ (Join)

#29.

A. 务 1. Kū (Skull without skin or hair)

B. 反 2. Lǎng (Light)

C. 仇 3. Záo (Chisel)

D. 凿 4. Wù (Affair)

E. 朗 5. Chóu (Hatred)

F. 骷 6. Fǎn (Anti-)

#30.

A. 赛 1. Wù (Fog)

B. 雾 2. Ài (Hinder)

C. 碍 3. Sài (Match)

D. 悸 4. Jì (Throb with terror)

E. 翘 5. Rén (Benevolence)

F. 仁 6. Qiáo (Raise)

CHAPTER 2: QUESTIONS (31-60)

#31.

A. 耩 1. Shàng (Still)

B. 族 2. Bì (To compare)

C. 体 3. Zú (Race)

D. 毕 4. Jiǎng (Sow with a drill)

E. 仙 5. Xiān (Celestial being)

F. 尚 6. Tǐ (Body)

#32.

A. 厄 1. È (Strategic point)

B. 夐 2. Chá (A badger-like wild animal)

C. 虎 3. Jiǔ (Collective term for the tribes of northern China during the Liao, Jin, and Yuan periods)

D. 纠 4. Xiòng (A surname)

E. 猹 5. Zhēn (Loyal)

F. 贞 6. Hǔ (Tiger)

#33.

A. 意 1. Yì (Meaning)

B. 辟 2. Xīn (Strong and pervasive fragrance)

C. 馨 3. Kǒng (Hole)

D. 倡 4. Chàng (Advocate)

E. 叫 5. Bì (Monarch)

F. 孔 6. Jiào (Cry)

#34.

A. 聂 1. Qí (Fork)

B. 异 2. Yì (Friendship)

C. 种 3. Niè (Whisper to)

D. 笛 4. Dí (Bamboo flute)

E. 谊 5. Yì (Different)

F. 歧 6. Chóng (A surname)

#35.

A. 辈 1. Guā (Shave)

B. 来 2. Bèi (Generation in family)

C. 彦 3. Yàn (A man of virtue and ability)

D. 肖 4. Shān (Delete)

E. 删 5. Lái (Come)

F. 刮 6. Xiāo (A surname)

#36.

A. 贡　　1. Tiáo ((Of a child) shed baby (or milk) teeth)

B. 旷　　2. Chù (Place)

C. 处　　3. Diǎo (Penis)

D. 掣　　4. Kuàng (Vast)

E. 屌　　5. Gòng (Pay tribute)

F. 龆　　6. Chè (Pull)

#37.

A. 叫　　1. Sī (Cool breeze)

B. 恐　　2. Wǎn (As if)

C. 忑　　3. Tè (Disturbed)

D. 飔　　4. Chī (Demons)

E. 宛　　5. Jiào (Cry)

F. 魑　　6. Kǒng (Fear)

#38.

A. 彩　　1. Tián (Till)

B. 棠　　2. Xuàn (Jade)

C. 提　　3. Táng (A surname)

D. 皋　　4. Gāo (Marshland)

E. 琄　　5. Cǎi (Variegated color)

F. 畋

6. Tí (Raise)

#39.

A. 洌

B. 鲍

C. 彦

D. 轱

E. 浇

F. 弆

1. Bào (Abalone)

2. Jiāo (Pour liquid on)

3. Gū (Vehicle)

4. Liè (Crystal-clear)

5. Yàn (Elegant)

6. Jǔ (Collect)

#40.

A. 洱

B. 惨

C. 贱

D. 舰

E. 聚

F. 毙

1. Jiàn (Cheap)

2. Ěr (Er He River (in Henan Province))

3. Jù (Assemble)

4. Jiàn (Warship)

5. Bì (Fall down)

6. Cǎn (Miserable)

#41.

A. 軒

B. 悸

1. Hán (Case)

2. Tǎn (Level)

C. 魁 | 3. Piāo (Rob)

D. 剽 | 4. Qián (In place names)

E. 函 | 5. Jì (Throb with terror)

F. 坦 | 6. Kuí (Chief)

#42.

A. 恶 | 1. Zhū (Bright red)

B. 泅 | 2. Juàn (Bird catching net)

C. 座 | 3. Dàn (Ball)

D. 罥 | 4. È (Evil)

E. 朱 | 5. Zuò (Seat)

F. 弹 | 6. Qiú (Swim)

#43.

A. 疙 | 1. Xìng (Nature)

B. 屏 | 2. Píng (Screen)

C. 沦 | 3. Lún (Sink)

D. 沧 | 4. Cāng ((Of the sea) dark blue)

E. 济 | 5. Gē (Wart)

F. 性 | 6. Jǐ (The Ji River)

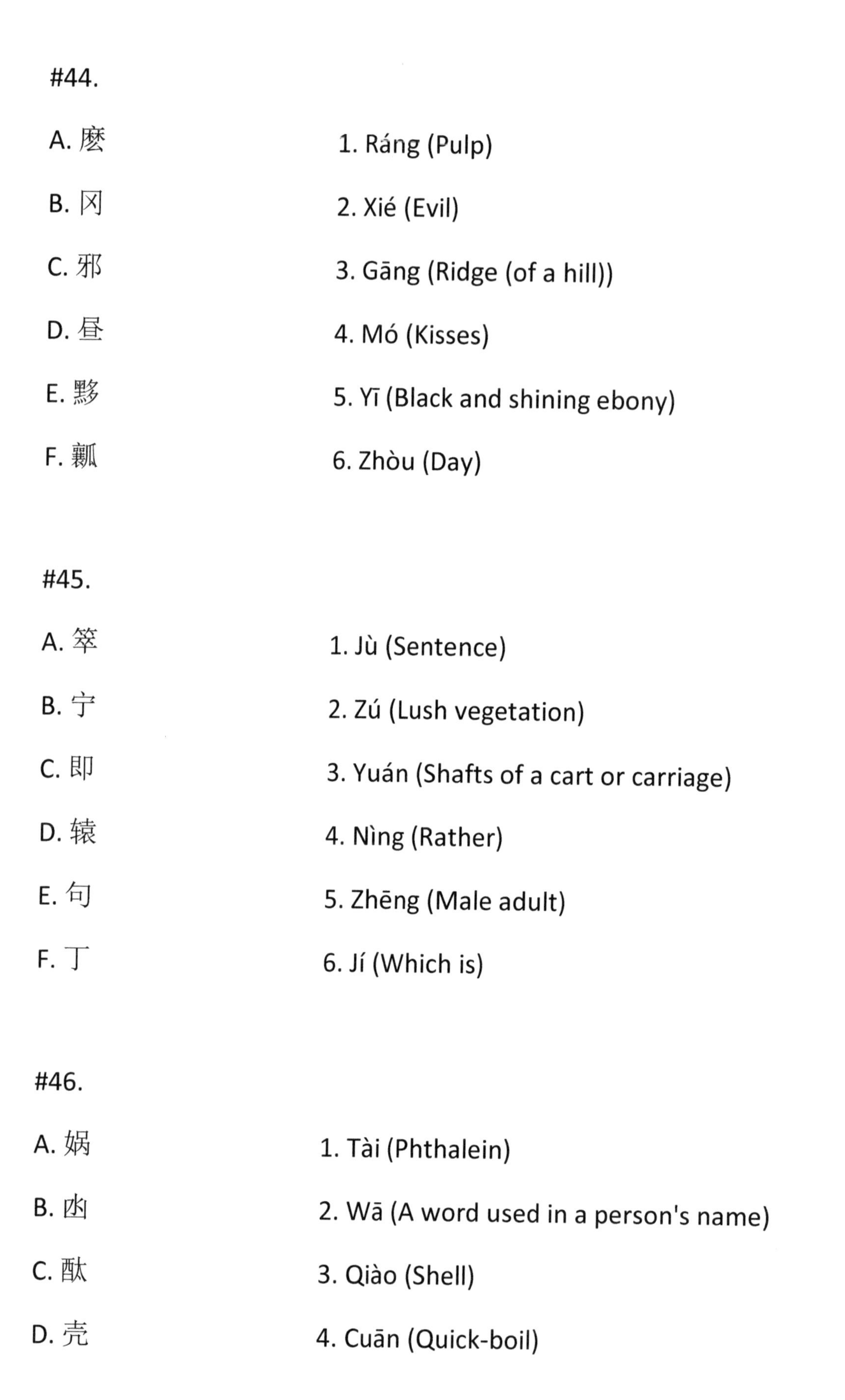

#44.

A. 麽 1. Ráng (Pulp)

B. 冈 2. Xié (Evil)

C. 邪 3. Gāng (Ridge (of a hill))

D. 昼 4. Mó (Kisses)

E. 黟 5. Yī (Black and shining ebony)

F. 瓤 6. Zhòu (Day)

#45.

A. 箤 1. Jù (Sentence)

B. 宁 2. Zú (Lush vegetation)

C. 即 3. Yuán (Shafts of a cart or carriage)

D. 辕 4. Nìng (Rather)

E. 句 5. Zhēng (Male adult)

F. 丁 6. Jí (Which is)

#46.

A. 娲 1. Tài (Phthalein)

B. 凼 2. Wā (A word used in a person's name)

C. 酞 3. Qiào (Shell)

D. 壳 4. Cuān (Quick-boil)

E. 氽　　5. Bǎ (Target)

F. 靶　　6. Dàng (Water puddle)

#47.

A. 勒　　1. Hú (Complete a set in mahjong)

B. 和　　2. Qiān (A footpath between fields, running north and south)

C. 孢　　3. Lēi (Tie or strap sth. tight)

D. 要　　4. Bāo (Spore)

E. 竜　　5. Lóng (Dragon)

F. 阡　　6. Yāo (Demand)

#48.

A. 銮　　1. Zhān (Wet)

B. 雷　　2. Lí (Li, a unit of length)

C. 厘　　3. Léi (Thunder)

D. 谥　　4. Luán (An imperial carriage)

E. 沾　　5. Shì (Posthumous title)

F. 潮　　6. Cháo (Tide)

#49.

A. 费　　1. Cuān (Quick-boil)

B. 脊 2. gé (Clams)

C. 蛤 3. Fèi (Fee)

D. 掴 4. Jí (Spine)

E. 氽 5. Guāi (Slap)

F. 州 6. Zhōu (An ancient administrative division)

#50.

A. 粪 1. Fèn (Droppings)

B. 亡 2. Yí (Maltose)

C. 科 3. Dòng (Freeze)

D. 巽 4. Wáng (Flee)

E. 冻 5. Kē (A branch of academic or vocational study)

F. 饴 6. Xùn (Xun, one of the Eight Diagrams)

#51.

A. 有 1. Zhào (Cover)

B. 罩 2. Zōu (Corner)

C. 鲑 3. Yǒu (Have)

D. 勒 4. Xiè (The legendary god sheep)

E. 璪 5. Zǎo (Silk tassels threaded with jades hanging from a coronet)

F. 陬　　6. Lè (Rein in)

#52.

A. 蕨　　1. Mèng (The first month)

B. 套　　2. Tào (Overlap)

C. 教　　3. Bī (Vaginal orifice)

D. 屄　　4. Nián (Sticky)

E. 孟　　5. Jiāo (Teach)

F. 黏　　6. Jué (Pteridium aquilinum var.)

#53.

A. 豭　　1. Běn (Stem or root of plants)

B. 转　　2. Jiā (Boar)

C. 氽　　3. Tǔn (Float)

D. 恢　　4. Zhuàn (Revolve)

E. 孽　　5. Huī (Extensive)

F. 本　　6. Niè (Evil)

#54.

A. 耐　　1. Lǒng (Cover)

B. 尥　　2. Nài (Be able to bear)

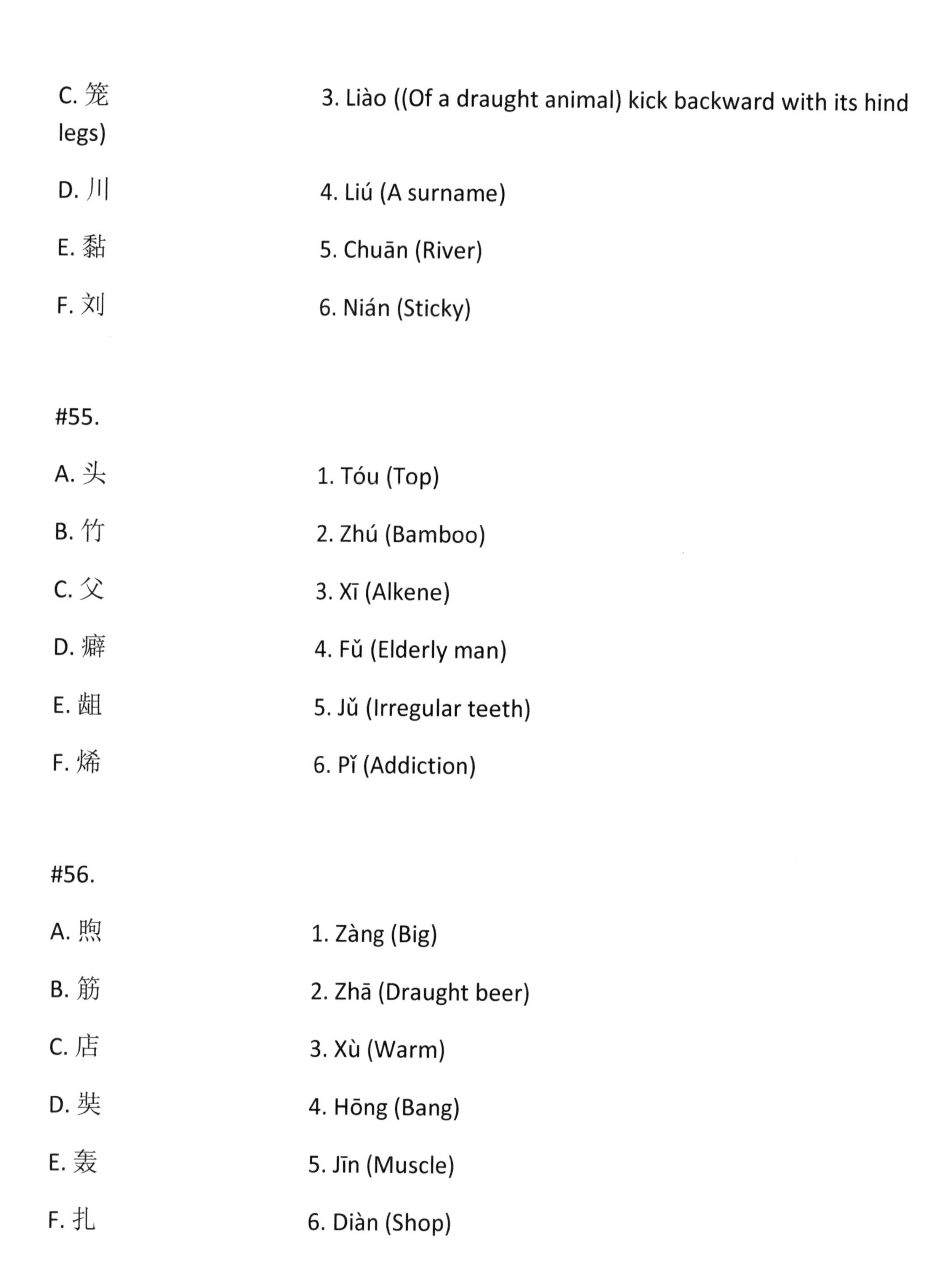

C. 笼 3. Liào ((Of a draught animal) kick backward with its hind legs)

D. 川 4. Liú (A surname)

E. 黏 5. Chuān (River)

F. 刘 6. Nián (Sticky)

#55.

A. 头 1. Tóu (Top)

B. 竹 2. Zhú (Bamboo)

C. 父 3. Xī (Alkene)

D. 癖 4. Fǔ (Elderly man)

E. 龃 5. Jǔ (Irregular teeth)

F. 烯 6. Pǐ (Addiction)

#56.

A. 煦 1. Zàng (Big)

B. 筋 2. Zhā (Draught beer)

C. 店 3. Xù (Warm)

D. 奘 4. Hōng (Bang)

E. 轰 5. Jīn (Muscle)

F. 扎 6. Diàn (Shop)

#57.

A. 郴 1. Jì (Cross a river)

B. 黔 2. Ruò (Weak)

C. 弱 3. Wèi (Place)

D. 济 4. Chēn (A surname)

E. 胜 5. Qián (Black)

F. 位 6. Shèng (Win)

#58.

A. 北 1. Chuán (Boat)

B. 渗 2. Shà (A tall building)

C. 舡 3. Shèn (Infiltrate)

D. 厦 4. Jìshēng (Garbage)

E. 转 5. Běi (North)

F. 圾 6. Zhuǎn (Change)

#59.

A. 沚 1. Wàn (A surname)

B. 曼 2. Zhǎn (Small cup)

C. 绳 3. Zhǐ (Small islets)

D. 瓮　　4. Wèng (Urn)

E. 缳　　5. Shéng (Rope)

F. 盏　　6. Huán (Tie around with ropes)

#60.

A. 怂　　1. Sǒng (Frightened)

B. 留　　2. Cháo (Tide)

C. 邿　　3. Liú (Remain)

D. 过　　4. Guò (Cross)

E. 排　　5. Shī (Shi, a state in the Zhou Dynasty)

F. 潮　　6. Pái (Row)

CHAPTER 3: QUESTIONS (61-90)

#61.

A. 剐 — 1. Bēi (Sad)

B. 欸 — 2. Hān (To one's heart's content)

C. 只 — 3. Guǎ (Cut into pieces)

D. 悲 — 4. Zhǐ (Only)

E. 絷 — 5. Ēi (Hey)

F. 酣 — 6. Zhí (Tie)

#62.

A. 沉 — 1. Jiǒng (In straitened circumstances)

B. 卷 — 2. Tāi (Short for Taizhou)

C. 释 — 3. Chén (Sink)

D. 台 — 4. Juàn (Volume)

E. 骁 — 5. Shì (Explain)

F. 窘 — 6. Xiāo (Valiant)

#63.

A. 燕 — 1. Chēng (Red)

B. 契 — 2. Bà (Chief of feudal princes)

C. 霸 3. Chá (Tea plant)

D. 赖 4. Qì (Contract)

E. 茶 5. Zhān (Glue)

F. 粘 6. Yàn (Swallow)

#64.

A. 席 1. Lián (Inexpensive)

B. 渤 2. Cuō (To twist)

C. 廉 3. Xí (Seat)

D. 旷 4. Bó (Bohai Sea)

E. 搓 5. Jiā (Boar)

F. 豭 6. Kuàng (Vast)

#65.

A. 即 1. Kǒng (Hole)

B. 矻 2. Éi (Sigh)

C. 划 3. Kū (Toil)

D. 欸 4. Pàn (Melt)

E. 泮 5. Huà (Delimit)

F. 孔 6. Jí (Which is)

#66.

A. 起 1. Fù (Pay)

B. 蚬 2. Xiè (Crab)

C. 付 3. Xuàn (Dazzle)

D. 蟹 4. Xiǎn (A species of small clam living in fresh water)

E. 泾 5. Qǐ (Rise)

F. 炫 6. Jīng (Short for the Jinghe River)

#67.

A. 关 1. Tǎn (Level)

B. 考 2. Guān (Turn off)

C. 灸 3. Jiǔ (Cauterize)

D. 饕 4. Kǎo (Test)

E. 黧 5. Tāo (Covetous)

F. 坦 6. Lí ((Usually of complexion) black)

#68.

A. 没 1. Méi (No)

B. 凛 2. Gāng (Hard)

C. 蝙 3. Lǐn (Cold)

D. 粡 4. Pò (Dregs of rice)

E. 粕　　5. Wān (Carve out)

F. 刚　　6. Biān (Bats)

#69.

A. 屦　　1. Fǔ (Axe)

B. 刺　　2. Jù (According to)

C. 桃　　3. Zì (Bones with rotten flesh)

D. 据　　4. Táo (Peach)

E. 胔　　5. Cì (Stab)

F. 斧　　6. Jù (Straw sandals)

#70.

A. 孤　　1. Xiāng (Fragrant)

B. 香　　2. Gū (Orphan)

C. 些　　3. Chuāi (Hide things in one's clothes)

D. 灭　　4. Xiē (Some)

E. 揣　　5. Jiě (Separate)

F. 解　　6. Miè (Extinguish)

#71.

A. 旬　　1. Líng (Zero)

B. 那 2. Pò (Amber)

C. 零 3. Pìn (Engage)

D. 够 4. Nà (That)

E. 聘 5. Gòu (Enough)

F. 珀 6. Xún (A period of ten days)

#72.

A. 町 1. Tīng (A word used in a place name)

B. 号 2. Cuò (Manage)

C. 稀 3. Xī (Rare)

D. 过 4. Nǎo (Brain)

E. 脑 5. Hào (Name)

F. 措 6. Guò (Cross)

#73.

A. 婷 1. Yuè (Yellowish-black)

B. 踹 2. Xīng (Prosper)

C. 弱 3. Tóng (Same)

D. 黦 4. Chuài (Kick)

E. 兴 5. Ruò (Weak)

F. 同 6. Tíng (Graceful)

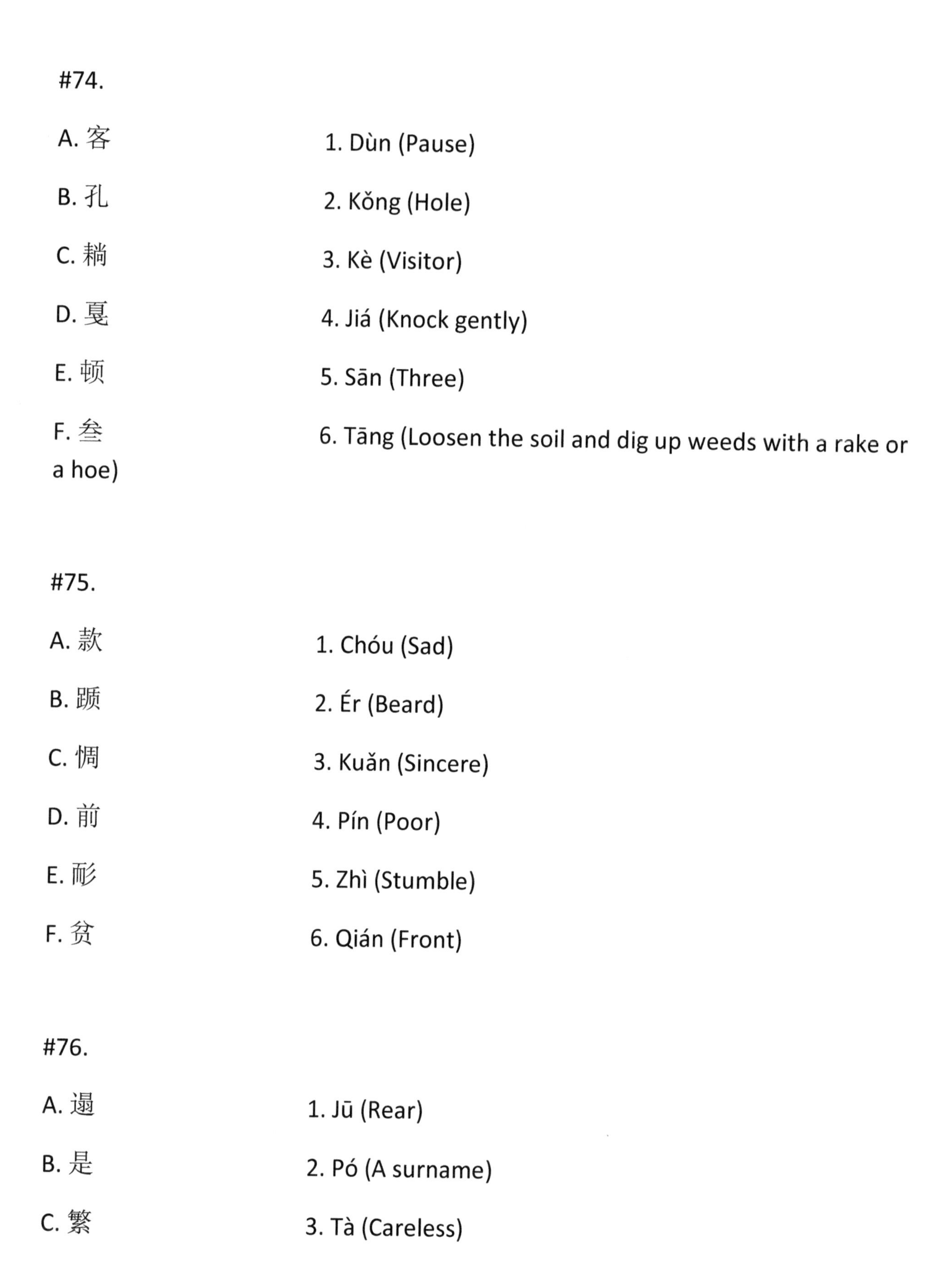

#74.

A. 客　　1. Dùn (Pause)

B. 孔　　2. Kǒng (Hole)

C. 耥　　3. Kè (Visitor)

D. 戛　　4. Jiá (Knock gently)

E. 顿　　5. Sān (Three)

F. 叁　　6. Tāng (Loosen the soil and dig up weeds with a rake or a hoe)

#75.

A. 款　　1. Chóu (Sad)

B. 踬　　2. Ér (Beard)

C. 惆　　3. Kuǎn (Sincere)

D. 前　　4. Pín (Poor)

E. 耏　　5. Zhì (Stumble)

F. 贫　　6. Qián (Front)

#76.

A. 遢　　1. Jū (Rear)

B. 是　　2. Pó (A surname)

C. 繁　　3. Tà (Careless)

D. 排 4. Pái (Row)

E. 鹿 5. Lù (Deer)

F. 鞠 6. Shì (Yes)

#77.

A. 雪 1. Nài (Be able to bear or endure)

B. 欸 2. Xuě (Snow)

C. 曲 3. Yǐn (Hide)

D. 毗 4. Èi (Sigh)

E. 耐 5. Qū (Bent)

F. 隐 6. Pí (Adjoin)

#78.

A. 南 1. Nán (South)

B. 鲇 2. Yā (Crow)

C. 鸦 3. Qiáo (Raise)

D. 翘 4. Nián (Catfish)

E. 出 5. Chū (Go out)

F. 沛 6. Bèi (A surname)

#79.

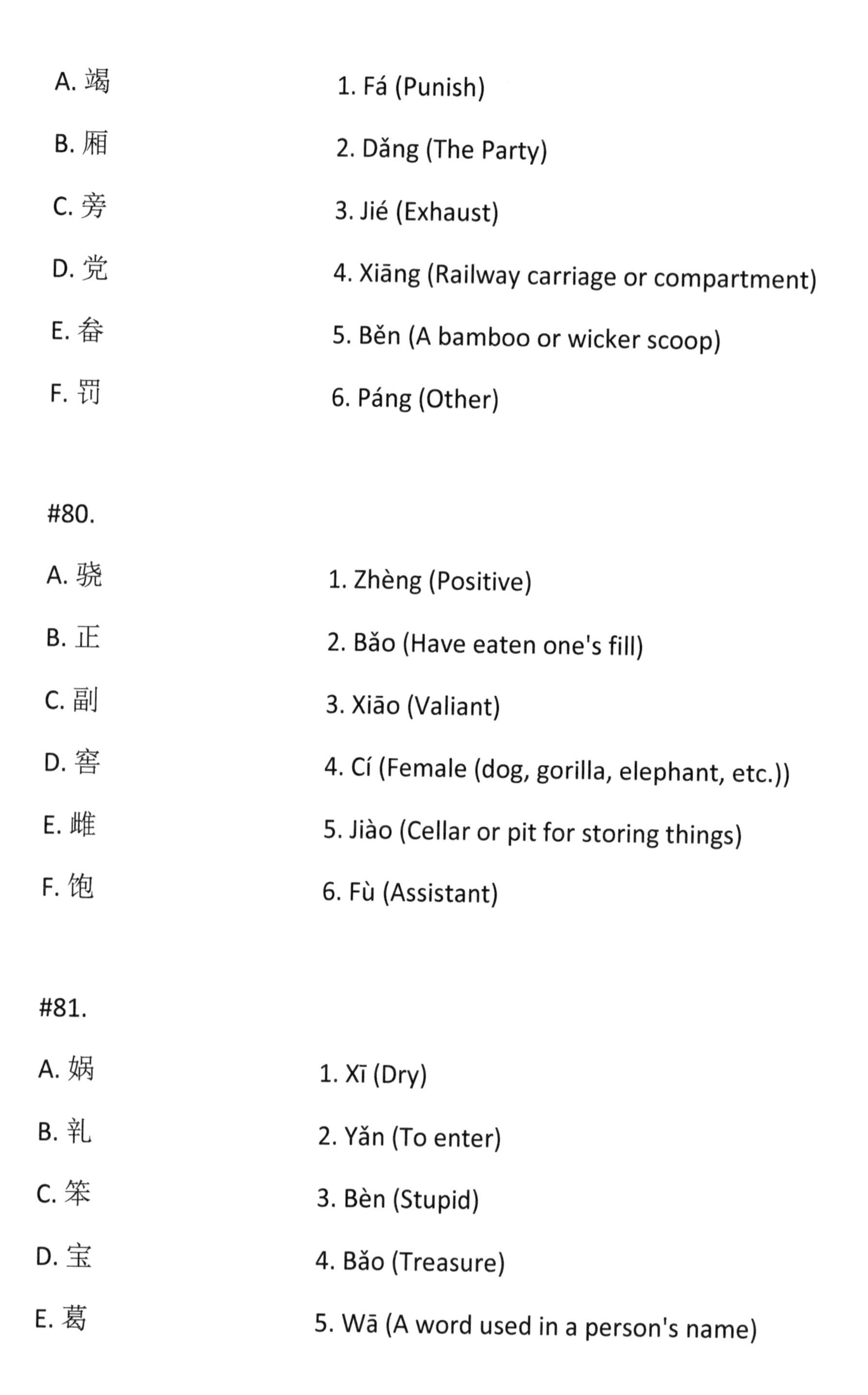

A. 竭

B. 厢

C. 旁

D. 党

E. 畚

F. 罚

1. Fá (Punish)
2. Dǎng (The Party)
3. Jié (Exhaust)
4. Xiāng (Railway carriage or compartment)
5. Běn (A bamboo or wicker scoop)
6. Páng (Other)

#80.

A. 骁

B. 正

C. 副

D. 窖

E. 雌

F. 饱

1. Zhèng (Positive)
2. Bǎo (Have eaten one's fill)
3. Xiāo (Valiant)
4. Cí (Female (dog, gorilla, elephant, etc.))
5. Jiào (Cellar or pit for storing things)
6. Fù (Assistant)

#81.

A. 娲

B. [illegible]

C. 笨

D. 宝

E. 葛

1. Xī (Dry)
2. Yǎn (To enter)
3. Bèn (Stupid)
4. Bǎo (Treasure)
5. Wā (A word used in a person's name)

F. 睎 | 6. Gé (Arrowroot)

#82.

A. 坷 | 1. Gū (Large fishing nets)

B. 媛 | 2. Xiāng (Each other)

C. 相 | 3. Kě (Bear the load)

D. 政 | 4. Zhèng (Politics)

E. 号 | 5. Háo (Howl)

F. 罛 | 6. Yuàn (Pretty girl)

#83.

A. 瓠 | 1. Hù (A kind of edible gourd)

B. 汲 | 2. Jí (Draw)

C. 盆 | 3. Lěi (Accumulate)

D. 累 | 4. Pén (Basin)

E. 可 | 5. Sān (Variant of 三)

F. 弎 | 6. Kě (Approve)

#84.

A. 硒 | 1. Zhì (Make)

B. 制 | 2. Yuán (A surname)

C. 钦 3. Xī (Selenium)

D. 伐 4. Xiè (Unlade)

E. 沅 5. Èi (Sigh)

F. 卸 6. Fá (Fell)

#85.

A. 艮 1. Bìng (Illness)

B. 病 2. Xiàn (County)

C. 县 3. gèn (One of the eight trigrams which represents the mountain)

D. 羲 4. Niè (Whisper to)

E. 龇 5. Xī (A surname)

F. 聂 6. Zī (Bare)

#86.

A. 恶 1. Wù (Dislike)

B. 耀 2. Zǒng (Assemble)

C. 凉 3. Yào (Shine)

D. 耷 4. Liáng (Cold)

E. 泯 5. Dā (Ears hanging down)

F. 总 6. Mǐn (Perish)

#87.

A. 罟 1. Xū (Dark)

B. 巡 2. Gǔ (Fish net)

C. 憬 3. Xún (Patrol)

D. 魆 4. Yāng (Mandarin duck)

E. 鸯 5. Zhǔ (Host)

F. 主 6. Jǐng (Awaken)

#88.

A. 腔 1. Qiāng (Cavity)

B. 耦 2. Shāo (A little)

C. 稍 3. Qìn (Ooze)

D. 败 4. Juéduì (Plough)

E. 漫 5. Bài (Defeat)

F. 沁 6. Màn (Overflow)

#89.

A. 乳 1. Nìng (Mud)

B. 采 2. Rǔ (Give birth to)

C. 备 3. Quán (Aldehyde)

D. 泞

E. 鸠

F. 醛

4. Cài (Feudal estate)

5. Jiū (Turtledove)

6. Bèi (Have)

#90.

A. 谐

B. 且

C. 鸨

D. 琵

E. 胥

F. 鞘

1. Qiě (Just)

2. Xū (Petty official)

3. Pí (In pí pá 琵琶)

4. Xié (In harmony)

5. Qiào (Sheath)

6. Bǎo (Bustard)

CHAPTER 4: QUESTIONS (91-120)

#91.

A. 沛 1. Jí (Gather)

B. 鳏 2. Guān (Huge fish)

C. 烦 3. Bèi (A surname)

D. 集 4. Lǚ (Repeatedly)

E. 屡 5. Fán (Trouble)

F. 欺 6. Qī (Deceive)

#92.

A. 孙 1. Hú (A dry measure used in former times, originally equal to 10 dou, later 5 dou)

B. 迈 2. Sūn (A surname)

C. 虢 3. Guó (Dukedom of Guo (a vassal state of the Zhou Dynasty))

D. 斛 4. Tí (Red wine)

E. 醍 5. Mài (Step)

F. 郇 6. Huán (Xun, a state in the Zhou Dynasty)

#93.

A. 包 1. Rán (Right)

B. 翌 2. Xiá (Flaw in a piece of jade)

C. 室 3. Yì (Immediately following in time)

D. 然 4. Bāo (Wrap)

E. 黠 5. Xiá (Crafty)

F. 瑕 6. Shì (Room)

#94.

A. 趣 1. Qù (Interest)

B. 须 2. Qìn (Ooze)

C. 沁 3. Xū (Must)

D. 勒 4. Lēi (Tie or strap sth. tight)

E. 教 5. Jiāo (Teach)

F. 他 6. Tā (He)

#95.

A. 开 1. Kāi (Open)

B. 放 2. Xiǎng (Feast)

C. 逼 3. Cǐ (This)

D. 此 4. Fàng (Release)

E. 荥 5. Xíng (The rising and dashing waves)

F. 飨 6. Bī (Force)

#96.

A. 教 | 1. Yú (What)
B. 龟 | 2. Guī (Tortoise)
C. 光 | 3. Jí (Which is)
D. 即 | 4. Guāng (Light)
E. 碑 | 5. Bēi (A stone tablet)
F. 於 | 6. Jiào (Religion)

#97.

A. 褛 | 1. Jiàn (Ancient bronze mirror)
B. 硭 | 2. Sī (This)
C. 鉴 | 3. Máng (A crude saltpeter)
D. 汹 | 4. Huí (Eddy)
E. 斯 | 5. Lǚ (Tattered)
F. 洄 | 6. Xiōng (Turbulent)

#98.

A. 的 | 1. Qī (Deceive)
B. 狰 | 2. Zhēng (A legendary leopard-like beast)
C. 欺 | 3. Dì (Target)

D. 粤 4. Yuè (Another name for Guangdong Province)

E. 凛 5. Lǐn (Cold)

F. 欺 6. Èi (Sigh)

#99.

A. 戴 1. Hú (Arc)

B. 合 2. Dài (Put on)

C. 殓 3. Liàn (Lay a body in a coffin)

D. 圠 4. Yà (Where the mountain bends)

E. 弧 5. Màn (Graceful)

F. 曼 6. Gě (Ge, a unit of dry measure for grain)

#100.

A. 褚 1. Zhǔ (Silk floss)

B. 勾 2. Gōu (Cancel)

C. 郓 3. Quǎn (A field ditch)

D. 耕 4. Gēng (Plough)

E. 畎 5. Cuī (Decrease)

F. 衰 6. Yùn (A surname)

#101.

A. 耜 | 1. Hǎ (Used in place names)
B. 魂 | 2. Shèng (Historical works)
C. 乘 | 3. Rán (Burn)
D. 燃 | 4. Tán (Shoot)
E. 畲 | 5. Sì (A spade-shaped farm tool used in ancient China)
F. 弹 | 6. Hún (Soul)

#102.

A. 凋 | 1. Huàn (Feed)
B. 营 | 2. Zhǎng (Rise)
C. 豢 | 3. Diāo (Withered)
D. 泻 | 4. Xún (A period of ten days)
E. 旬 | 5. Yíng (Seek)
F. 涨 | 6. Xiè (Flow swiftly)

#103.

A. 軒 | 1. Kuí (A surname)
B. 晟 | 2. Tǎ (Sole)
C. 隗 | 3. Quán (Counterpoise)
D. 权 | 4. Huái (Bosom)
E. 怀 | 5. Shèng (Bright)

F. 鳎　　6. Qián (In place names)

#104.

A. 硒　　1. Zhì (Place)

B. 临　　2. Lín (Be close to)

C. 驯　　3. Zhōu (An ancient administrative division)

D. 置　　4. Xún (Tame)

E. 琊　　5. Xī (Selenium)

F. 州　　6. Yá (A place in Shandong)

#105.

A. 舾　　1. Huá (Sly)

B. 沦　　2. Chū (Go out)

C. 猾　　3. Lún (Sink)

D. 握　　4. Kǎ (Card)

E. 卡　　5. Wò (Grip)

F. 出　　6. Xī (Ship equipment and installations)

#106.

A. 絜　　1. Zǎi (Year)

B. 载　　2. Jié (Clean)

C. 欺 3. Táng (A surname)

D. 肾 4. Qī (Deceive)

E. 棠 5. Shèn (Kidney)

F. 盅 6. Zhōng (Handleless cup)

#107.

A. 享 1. Jiǎn (Less)

B. 丞 2. Xiǎng (To enjoy)

C. 军 3. Jūn (Armed forces)

D. 宁 4. Chéng (Assist)

E. 洑 5. Fú (Undercurrent)

F. 减 6. Nìng (Rather)

#108.

A. 沵 1. Náo (A kind of gibbon)

B. 窜 2. Fēng (Beacon fire)

C. 伪 3. Mǐ ((Of water) full)

D. 夒 4. Fǎn (Reverse side)

E. 烽 5. Wěi (Pseudo)

F. 反 6. Cuàn (Flee)

#109.

A. 亡	1. Chóu (Propose a toast)
B. 断	2. Cún (Exist)
C. 登	3. Jīn (Jin, a unit of weight (0.5Kg))
D. 斤	4. Dēng (Board)
E. 酬	5. Yín (Gum)
F. 存	6. Wáng (Flee)

#110.

A. 奘	1. Zàng (Big)
B. 龌	2. Wò (Dirty)
C. 树	3. Dā (Ears hanging down)
D. 贡	4. Yǎ (Refined)
E. 耷	5. Gòng (Pay tribute)
F. 雅	6. Shù (Tree)

#111.

A. 唐	1. Wēi (River bend)
B. 縠	2. Hú (Crepe)
C. 隈	3. Wén (Character)
D. 文	4. Táng (The Tang Dynasty)

E. 霂 5. Xiàn (County)

F. 县 6. Mù (A light rain)

#112.

A. 账 1. Jìn (Cinder)

B. 轴 2. Yú (Corner)

C. 泊 3. Zhóu (Axle)

D. 烬 4. Zhàng (Account)

E. 隅 5. Bó (Lie at anchor)

F. 邗 6. Hán (Name of an ancient river)

#113.

A. 琏 1. Hū (Neglect)

B. 同 2. Jiǎng (Sow with a drill)

C. 殂 3. Cú (Die)

D. 云 4. Liǎn (An ancient vessel for broomcorn millet)

E. 耩 5. Tóng (Same)

F. 忽 6. Yún (Surname)

#114.

A. 敕 1. Jiào (Cellar or pit for storing things)

B. 灿 2. Càn (Bright)

C. 蛮 3. Dié (Septuagenarian)

D. 窖 4. Xián (Epilepsy)

E. 耋 5. Chì (Imperial order)

F. 痫 6. Mán (An ancient name for southern nationalities)

#115.

A. 阵 1. Mò (Footpaths among fields running east and west)

B. 陌 2. Nián (Catfish)

C. 鲇 3. Zhèn (Battle array)

D. 信 4. Xìn (Letter)

E. 上 5. Wā (A word used in a person's name)

F. 娲 6. Shàng (On)

#116.

A. 孢 1. Què (Sparrow)

B. 捂 2. Zhǐ (Purport)

C. 琅 3. Bāo (Spore)

D. 符 4. Wǔ (Seal)

E. 雀 5. Fú (Tally)

F. 旨 6. Láng (A surname)

#117.

A. 驮　　1. Duò (Pack)

B. 煞　　2. Căn (Miserable)

C. 臂　　3. Bì (Arm)

D. 膨　　4. Péng (Expand)

E. 惨　　5. Shà (Evil spirit)

F. 忠　　6. Zhōng (Loyal)

#118.

A. 盒　　1. Jiè (Boundary)

B. 昏　　2. Něi (Hungry)

C. 界　　3. Biàn (Distinguish)

D. 馁　　4. Hé (Box)

E. 堪　　5. Kān (May)

F. 辨　　6. Hūn (Dusk)

#119.

A. 咫　　1. Jiù (Even if)

B. 孵　　2. Chǐ (Tooth)

C. 痴　　3. Fū (Brood)

D. 就　　4. Wèi (Officer)

E. 尉　　5. Zhǐ (An ancient measure of length, equal to 8 cun)

F. 齿　　6. Chī (Silly)

#120.

A. 身　　1. Dǒu (Steep)

B. 辰　　2. Jīn (This)

C. 陡　　3. Chén (Time)

D. 缢　　4. Xiā (Shrimp)

E. 今　　5. Yì (Hang)

F. 虾　　6. Shēn (Body)

CHAPTER 5: QUESTIONS (121-150)

#121.

A. 座 1. Běn (A bamboo or wicker scoop)

B. 队 2. Xiǎng (Entertain)

C. 畚 3. Duì (A row of people)

D. 饷 4. Zuò (Seat)

E. 龄 5. Luàn (In a mess)

F. 乱 6. Líng (Age)

#122.

A. 电 1. Jiè (Boundary)

B. 霂 2. Mù (A light rain)

C. 氽 3. Diàn (Electricity)

D. 夭 4. Tǔn (Float)

E. 界 5. Yāo (Tender)

F. 戚 6. Qī (Relative)

#123.

A. 希 1. Chuán (Boat)

B. 不 2. Bù (Do not)

C. 舡　　3. Chān (Observe)

D. 觇　　4. Cú (Die)

E. 赪　　5. Xī (Hope)

F. 殂　　6. Chēng (Red)

#124.

A. 揣　　1. Chuāi (Hide things in one's clothes)

B. 洑　　2. Chì (Upbraid)

C. 斥　　3. Chéng (Ride)

D. 瓤　　4. Yù (Heal)

E. 愈　　5. Ráng (Pulp)

F. 乘　　6. Fú (Undercurrent)

#125.

A. 凹　　1. Hù (Freezing)

B. 煎　　2. Pá (Lute)

C. 另　　3. Wā (Low-lying area)

D. 沍　　4. Lìng (Another)

E. 琶　　5. Dài (Loan)

F. 贷　　6. Jiān (Fry in shallow oil)

#126.

A. 邡 1. Fāng (A word used in a place name)

B. 性 2. Shì (Be similar)

C. 驭 3. Gá (Press hard against each other)

D. 邠 4. Yù (Control)

E. 轧 5. Xìng (Nature)

F. 似 6. Bīn (A surname)

#127.

A. 昔 1. Xī (Former times)

B. 义 2. Kuài (A surname)

C. 郐 3. Yì (Justice)

D. 耔 4. Zǐ (To cultivate the soil (on plant roots))

E. 殊 5. Xiǎn (Wild fires)

F. 燹 6. Shū (Different)

#128.

A. 童 1. Bāng (State)

B. 谥 2. Shì (Posthumous title)

C. 邦 3. Juǎn (Embroil)

D. 鳔 4. Biào (Swim bladder of fish)

E. 蕨　　5. Tóng (Child)

F. 卷　　6. Jué (Pteridium aquilinum var.)

#129.

A. 飕　　1. Qī (Lean to one side)

B. 欹　　2. Sōu (Make sth. dry or cool)

C. 只　　3. Gāo (Lamb)

D. 羔　　4. Zhī (Single)

E. 凶　　5. Gōng (Attack)

F. 攻　　6. Xiōng (Inauspicious)

#130.

A. 郐　　1. Kuài (A surname)

B. 褪　　2. Jiāng (Support)

C. 竣　　3. Jùn (Complete)

D. 彦　　4. Tùn (Slip out of sth)

E. 拉　　5. Lā (Pull)

F. 将　　6. Yàn (Elegant)

#131.

A. 膏　　1. Fù (Attach)

B. 那　　2. Qián (Front)

C. 管　　3. Nèi (That)

D. 前　　4. Jùn (Complete)

E. 附　　5. Gāo (Fat)

F. 竣　　6. Guǎn (Pipe)

#132.

A. 奶　　1. Fēng (Wind)

B. 冉　　2. Gōu (Cancel)

C. 勾　　3. Hán (South Korea)

D. 辽　　4. Nǎi (Breasts)

E. 韩　　5. Rǎn (Edge of tortoise-shell)

F. 风　　6. Liáo (Distant)

#133.

A. 沉　　1. Nìng (Rather)

B. 泊　　2. Xī (Bright)

C. 魃　　3. Fěi (Bandit)

D. 匪　　4. Bá (A legendary evil spirit causing drought)

E. 宁　　5. Chén (Sink)

F. 熙　　6. Pō (Lake)

#134.

A. 殁 — 1. Shú (Redemption)

B. 详 — 2. Xiào (Smile)

C. 羲 — 3. Qín (A surname)

D. 笑 — 4. Xiáng (Detailed)

E. 赎 — 5. Xī (A surname)

F. 覃 — 6. Mò (Die)

#135.

A. 坛 — 1. Sòng (Song, a state in the Zhou Dynasty)

B. 媒 — 2. Tún (Stuffed dumplings)

C. 幽 — 3. Lí (Loriot)

D. 饨 — 4. Yōu (Deep and remote)

E. 宋 — 5. Tán (Altar)

F. 鹂 — 6. Méi (Matchmake)

#136.

A. 罕 — 1. Lěng (Cold)

B. 洱 — 2. Kè (Visitor)

C. 客 — 3. Zhài (Zhai, a state in the Zhou Dynasty)

D. 散　　4. Fú (Bird-net)

E. 冷　　5. Sǎn (Come loose)

F. 祭　　6. Ěr (Er He River (in Henan Province))

#137.

A. 踯　　1. Rǔ (Give birth to)

B. 乳　　2. Zhí (Pace up and down)

C. 竭　　3. Hàn (Weld)

D. 焊　　4. Jié (Exhaust)

E. 售　　5. Yǒng (Forever)

F. 永　　6. Shòu (Sell)

#138.

A. 戎　　1. Róng (Army)

B. 和　　2. Qiú (Spouse)

C. 废　　3. Shèng (Bright)

D. 晟　　4. Hú (Complete a set in mahjong)

E. 仇　　5. Fèi (Give up)

F. 雀　　6. Qiǎo (Sparrow)

#139.

A. 式 1. Sū (Rush out)

B. 窣 2. Zǐ (To cultivate the soil (on plant roots))

C. 登 3. Shì (Type)

D. 耔 4. Luán (Twin)

E. 申 5. Dēng (Board)

F. 孪 6. Shēn (State)

#140.

A. 扃 1. Xiōng (Inauspicious)

B. 缋 2. Xià (Frighten)

C. 桂 3. Guì (Cassia)

D. 吓 4. Mò (Socks)

E. 凶 5. Jiōng (A bolt or hook for fastening a door from outside)

F. 靺 6. Huì (Paint)

#141.

A. 扈 1. Bì (To compare)

B. 耔 2. Wù (Uncomfortable)

C. 翌 3. Yì (Immediately following in time)

D. 炫 4. Ěr (You)

E. 尔 5. Xuàn (Dazzle)

F. 坒　　6. Zǐ (To cultivate the soil (on plant roots))

#142.

A. 缤　　1. Fèi (Boil)

B. 迁　　2. Bīn (Abundant)

C. 漏　　3. Lòu (Leak)

D. 霎　　4. Shà (A very short time)

E. 鑫　　5. Xīn (Prosper in business)

F. 沸　　6. Qiān (Move)

#143.

A. 蜃　　1. Wěi (Entrust)

B. 烧　　2. Zhèng (Positive)

C. 委　　3. Shāo (Burn)

D. 正　　4. Qiè (Concubine)

E. 角　　5. Jué (Role)

F. 妾　　6. Shèn (Clams)

#144.

A. 狩　　1. Hé (River)

B. 那　　2. Zhǎ (Salted fish)

C. 盛 — 3. Yī (Doctor)

D. 河 — 4. Shèng (Flourishing)

E. 鲊 — 5. Shòu (Hunt in winter)

F. 医 — 6. Nā (A surname)

#145.

A. 予 — 1. Bān (Spot)

B. 脊 — 2. Dù (Ferry crossing)

C. 蒜 — 3. Yú (I)

D. 陲 — 4. Suàn (Garlic)

E. 斑 — 5. Jí (Spine)

F. 渡 — 6. Chuí (Frontiers)

#146.

A. 富 — 1. Căn (Dark)

B. 宦 — 2. Jiù (Chronic illness)

C. 弘 — 3. Zā (Circumference)

D. 疚 — 4. Hóng (Great)

E. 黪 — 5. Huàn (Official)

F. 匝 — 6. Fù (Wealth)

#147.

A. 油 1. Kǒng (Hole)

B. 裸 2. Tiān (Day)

C. 宥 3. Máng (Blind)

D. 盲 4. Yòu (Pardon)

E. 孔 5. Yóu (Oil)

F. 天 6. Luǒ (Exposed)

#148.

A. 丹 1. Chú (Young)

B. 觚 2. Gū (Goblet with a broad lip, long narrow stem, and flared base)

C. 獒 3. Dān (Ref)

D. 雏 4. Zì (A large piece of meat)

E. 晕 5. Yùn (Halo)

F. 胾 6. Áo (Mastiff)

#149.

A. 申 1. Shēn (State)

B. 洞 2. Lóng (Gallery)

C. 窿 3. Cāng ((Of the sea) dark blue)

D. 致 4. Jiǒng (Far)

E. 沧 5. Zhì (Deliver)

F. 舨 6. Bǎn (Small boat)

#150.

A. 颍 1. Chéng (Rule)

B. 程 2. Hǎi (Sea)

C. 采 3. Cǎi (Pick)

D. 斛 4. Yǐng (Name of a river in Henan and Anhui)

E. 海 5. Háo (Raccoon dog)

F. 貉 6. Hú (A dry measure used in former times, originally equal to 10 dou, later 5 dou)

ANSWERS (1-150)

#1.	F. Qiǎng	D. Gāo	B. Qián	#76.	F. Tā	D. Yún	B. Rǎn
A. Chuāng		E. Xuàn	C. Ruò	A. Tà		E. Jiǎng	C. Gōu
B. Zhù	#20.	F. Tián	D. Jì	B. Shì	#95.	F. Hū	D. Liáo
C. Bàng	A. Xù		E. Shèng	C. Pó	A. Kāi		E. Hán
D. Fén	B. Níng	#39.	F. Wèi	D. Pái	B. Fàng	#114.	F. Fēng
E. Kān	C. Dàng	A. Liè		E. Lù	C. Bī	A. Chì	
F. Guì	D. Zhàn	B. Bào	#58.	F. Jū	D. Cǐ	B. Càn	#133.
	E. Gū	C. Yàn	A. Běi		E. Xíng	C. Mán	A. Chén
#2.	F. Qiū	D. Gū	B. Shèn	#77.	F. Xiǎng	D. Jiào	B. Pō
A. Yín		E. Jiāo	C. Chuán	A. Xuě		E. Dié	C. Bá
B. Tí	#21.	F. Jǔ	D. Shà	B. Èi	#96.	F. Xián	D. Fěi
C. Qíng	A. Què		E. Zhuǎn	C. Qū	A. Jiào		E. Nìng
D. Sù	B. Ruì	#40.	F. Jìshēng	D. Pí	B. Guī	#115.	F. Xī
E. Shāo	C. Lěi	A. Ěr		E. Nài	C. Guāng	A. Zhèn	
F. Jiē	D. Xún	B. Cǎn	#59.	F. Yǐn	D. Jí	B. Mò	#134.
	E. Yù	C. Jiàn	A. Zhǐ		E. Bēi	C. Nián	A. Mò
#3.	F. Yù	D. Jiàn	B. Wàn	#78.	F. Yú	D. Xìn	B. Xiáng
A. Guì		E. Jù	C. Shéng	A. Nán		E. Shàng	C. Xī
B. Gā	#22.	F. Bì	D. Wèng	B. Nián	#97.	F. Wā	D. Xiào
C. Ruò	A. Yì		E. Huán	C. Yā	A. Lǚ		E. Shú
D. Huī	B. Cū	#41.	F. Zhǎn	D. Qiáo	B. Máng	#116.	F. Qín
E. Kè	C. Shuò	A. Qián		E. Chū	C. Jiàn	A. Bāo	
F. Wèi	D. Gòng	B. Jì	#60.	F. Bèi	D. Xiōng	B. Wǔ	#135.
	E. Yì	C. Kuí	A. Sǒng		E. Sī	C. Láng	A. Tán
#4.	F. Háo	D. Piāo	B. Liú	#79.	F. Huí	D. Fú	B. Méi
A. Jì		E. Hán	C. Shī	A. Jié		E. Què	C. Yōu
B. Yuè	#23.	F. Tǎn	D. Guò	B. Xiāng	#98.	F. Zhǐ	D. Tún
C. Bèi	A. Pù		E. Pái	C. Páng	A. Dì		E. Sòng
D. Hàng	B. Dòng	#42.	F. Cháo	D. Dǎng	B. Zhēng	#117.	F. Lí
E. Yǐ	C. Chuāi	A. È		E. Běn	C. Èi	A. Duò	

F. Yǎo	D. Tián	B. Qiú	#61.	F. Fá	D. Yuè	B. Shà	#136.
	E. Bà	C. Zuò	A. Guǎ		E. Lǐn	C. Bì	A. Fú
#5.	F. Shì	D. Juàn	B. Ēi	#80.	F. Qī	D. Péng	B. Ěr
A. Yàn		E. Zhū	C. Zhǐ	A. Xiāo		E. Cǎn	C. Kè
B. Gū	#24.	F. Dàn	D. Bēi	B. Zhèng	#99.	F. Zhōng	D. Sǎn
C. Qǔ	A. Jiāng		E. Zhí	C. Fù	A. Dài		E. Lěng
D. Lì	B. Yù	#43.	F. Hān	D. Jiào	B. Gě	#118.	F. Zhài
E. Zhuī	C. Qī	A. Gē		E. Cí	C. Liàn	A. Hé	
F. Qín	D. Yīn	B. Píng	#62.	F. Bǎo	D. Yà	B. Hūn	#137.
	E. Liè	C. Lún	A. Chén		E. Hú	C. Jiè	A. Zhí
#6.	F. Mù	D. Cāng	B. Juàn	#81.	F. Màn	D. Něi	B. Rǔ
A. Nè		E. Jǐ	C. Shì	A. Wā		E. Kān	C. Jié
B. Hén	#25.	F. Xìng	D. Tāi	B. Yǎn	#100.	F. Biàn	D. Hàn
C. Qiān	A. Mèi		E. Xiāo	C. Bèn	A. Zhǔ		E. Shòu
D. Wū	B. Yì	#44.	F. Jiǒng	D. Bǎo	B. Gōu	#119.	F. Yǒng
E. Gé	C. Hǔ	A. Mó		E. Gé	C. Yùn	A. Zhǐ	
F. Suí	D. Hū	B. Gāng	#63.	F. Xī	D. Gēng	B. Fū	#138.
	E. Yìn	C. Xié	A. Yàn		E. Quǎn	C. Chī	A. Róng
#7.	F. Qué	D. Zhòu	B. Qì	#82.	F. Cuī	D. Jiù	B. Hú
A. Zhàng		E. Yī	C. Bà	A. Kě		E. Wèi	C. Fèi
B. Shù	#26.	F. Ráng	D. Chēng	B. Yuàn	#101.	F. Chǐ	D. Shèng
C. Xù	A. Kù		E. Chá	C. Xiāng	A. Sì		E. Qiú
D. Zhēng	B. Jīng	#45.	F. Zhān	D. Zhèng	B. Hún	#120.	F. Qiǎo
E. Jiù	C. Lóng	A. Zú		E. Háo	C. Shèng	A. Shēn	
F. Qián	D. Zhòu	B. Nìng	#64.	F. Gū	D. Rán	B. Chén	#139.
	E. Bàng	C. Jí	A. Xí		E. Hǎ	C. Dǒu	A. Shì
#8.	F. Jiàn	D. Yuán	B. Bó	#83.	F. Tán	D. Yì	B. Sū
A. Shǐ		E. Jù	C. Lián	A. Hù		E. Jīn	C. Dēng
B. Qī	#27.	F. Zhēng	D. Kuàng	B. Jí	#102.	F. Xiā	D. Zǐ
C. Shǎng	A. Le		E. Cuō	C. Pén	A. Diāo		E. Shēn

D. Chóng	B. Jī	#46.	F. Jiā	D. Lěi	B. Yíng	#121.	F. Luán
E. Bié	C. Ōu	A. Wā		E. Kě	C. Huàn	A. Zuò	
F. Jiè	D. Máng	B. Dàng	#65.	F. Sān	D. Xiè	B. Duì	#140.
	E. Tū	C. Tài	A. Jí		E. Xún	C. Běn	A. Jiōng
#9.	F. Máng	D. Qiào	B. Kū	#84.	F. Zhǎng	D. Xiǎng	B. Huì
A. Bà		E. Cuān	C. Huà	A. Xī		E. Líng	C. Guì
B. Zhì	#28.	F. Bǎ	D. Éi	B. Zhì	#103.	F. Luàn	D. Xià
C. Kāi	A. Chén		E. Pàn	C. Èi	A. Qián		E. Xiōng
D. Nuò	B. Pì	#47.	F. Kǒng	D. Fá	B. Shèng	#122.	F. Mò
E. Yǐn	C. Yòu	A. Lēi		E. Yuán	C. Kuí	A. Diàn	
F. Xī	D. Zhǔ	B. Hú	#66.	F. Xiè	D. Quán	B. Mù	#141.
	E. Líng	C. Bāo	A. Qǐ		E. Huái	C. Tǔn	A. Wù
#10.	F. Sī	D. Yāo	B. Xiǎn	#85.	F. Tǎ	D. Yāo	B. Zǐ
A. Guī		E. Lóng	C. Fù	A. gèn		E. Jiè	C. Yì
B. Jiào	#29.	F. Qiān	D. Xiè	B. Bìng	#104.	F. Qī	D. Xuàn
C. Xī	A. Wù		E. Jīng	C. Xiàn	A. Xī		E. Ěr
D. Suǒ	B. Fǎn	#48.	F. Xuàn	D. Xī	B. Lín	#123.	F. Bì
E. Xūn	C. Chóu	A. Luán		E. Zī	C. Xún	A. Xī	
F. Zāng	D. Záo	B. Léi	#67.	F. Niè	D. Zhì	B. Bù	#142.
	E. Lǎng	C. Lí	A. Guān		E. Yá	C. Chuán	A. Bīn
#11.	F. Kū	D. Shì	B. Kǎo	#86.	F. Zhōu	D. Chān	B. Qiān
A. Bó		E. Zhān	C. Jiǔ	A. Wù		E. Chēng	C. Lòu
B. Huì	#30.	F. Cháo	D. Tāo	B. Yào	#105.	F. Cú	D. Shà
C. Quán	A. Sài		E. Lí	C. Liáng	A. Xī		E. Xīn
D. Gāng	B. Wù	#49.	F. Tǎn	D. Dā	B. Lún	#124.	F. Fèi
E. Mèi	C. Ài	A. Fèi		E. Mǐn	C. Huá	A. Chuāi	
F. Duì	D. Jì	B. Jí	#68.	F. Zǒng	D. Wò	B. Fú	#143.
	E. Qiáo	C. gé	A. Méi		E. Kǎ	C. Chì	A. Shèn
#12.	F. Rén	D. Guāi	B. Lǐn	#87.	F. Chū	D. Ráng	B. Shāo
A. Méng		E. Cuān	C. Biān	A. Gǔ		E. Yù	C. Wěi
B. Jīn	#31.	F. Zhōu	D. Wān	B. Xún	#106.	F. Chéng	D. Zhèng
C. Kuài	A. Jiǎng		E. Pò	C. Jǐng	A. Jié		E. Jué

D. Jiū	B. Zú	#50.	F. Gāng	D. Xū	B. Zǎi	#125.	F. Qiè
E. Chuǎi	C. Tī	A. Fèn		E. Yāng	C. Qī	A. Wā	
F. Yíng	D. Bì	B. Wáng	#69.	F. Zhǔ	D. Shèn	B. Jiān	#144.
	E. Xiān	C. Kē	A. Jù		E. Táng	C. Lìng	A. Shòu
#13.	F. Shàng	D. Xùn	B. Cì	#88.	F. Zhōng	D. Hù	B. Nā
A. Yī		E. Dòng	C. Táo	A. Qiāng		E. Pá	C. Shèng
B. Chòu	#32.	F. Yí	D. Jù	B. Juéduì	#107.	F. Dài	D. Hé
C. Dí	A. È		E. Zì	C. Shāo	A. Xiǎng		E. Zhǎ
D. Chèn	B. Xiòng	#51.	F. Fǔ	D. Bài	B. Chéng	#126.	F. Yī
E. Róng	C. Hǔ	A. Yǒu		E. Màn	C. Jūn	A. Fāng	
F. Zǐ	D. Jiǔ	B. Zhào	#70.	F. Qìn	D. Nìng	B. Xìng	#145.
	E. Chá	C. Xiè	A. Gū		E. Fú	C. Yù	A. Yú
#14.	F. Zhēn	D. Lè	B. Xiāng	#89.	F. Jiǎn	D. Bīn	B. Jí
A. Shèng		E. Zǎo	C. Xiē	A. Rǔ		E. Gá	C. Suàn
B. Miè	#33.	F. Zōu	D. Miè	B. Cài	#108.	F. Shì	D. Chuí
C. Kān	A. Yì		E. Chuāi	C. Bèi	A. Mǐ		E. Bān
D. Jiàng	B. Bì	#52.	F. Jiě	D. Nìng	B. Cuàn	#127.	F. Dù
E. Sōng	C. Xīn	A. Jué		E. Jiū	C. Wěi	A. Xī	
F. Guāi	D. Chàng	B. Tào	#71.	F. Quán	D. Náo	B. Yì	#146.
	E. Jiào	C. Jiāo	A. Xún		E. Fēng	C. Kuài	A. Fù
#15.	F. Kǒng	D. Bī	B. Nà	#90.	F. Fǎn	D. Zǐ	B. Huàn
A. Wà		E. Mèng	C. Líng	A. Xié		E. Shū	C. Hóng
B. Yíng	#34.	F. Nián	D. Gòu	B. Qiě	#109.	F. Xiǎn	D. Jiù
C. Zuàn	A. Niè		E. Pìn	C. Bǎo	A. Wáng		E. Cǎn
D. Suān	B. Yì	#53.	F. Pò	D. Pí	B. Yín	#128.	F. Zā
E. Wò	C. Chóng	A. Jiā		E. Xū	C. Dēng	A. Tóng	
F. Xié	D. Dí	B. Zhuàn	#72.	F. Qiào	D. Jīn	B. Shì	#147.

	E. Yì	C. Tǔn	A. Tīng		E. Chóu	C. Bāng	A. Yóu
#16.	F. Qí	D. Huī	B. Hào	#91.	F. Cún	D. Biào	B. Luǒ
A. Lún		E. Niè	C. Xī	A. Bèi		E. Jué	C. Yòu
B. Gōng	#35.	F. Běn	D. Guò	B. Guān	#110.	F. Juǎn	D. Máng
C. Hēng	A. Bèi		E. Nǎo	C. Fán	A. Zàng		E. Kǒng
D. Yǐn	B. Lái	#54.	F. Cuò	D. Jí	B. Wò	#129.	F. Tiān
E. Xī	C. Yàn	A. Nài		E. Lǚ	C. Shù	A. Sōu	
F. Ài	D. Xiāo	B. Liào	#73.	F. Qī	D. Gòng	B. Qī	#148.
	E. Shān	C. Lǒng	A. Tíng		E. Dā	C. Zhī	A. Dān
#17.	F. Guā	D. Chuān	B. Chuài	#92.	F. Yǎ	D. Gāo	B. Gū
A. Jié		E. Nián	C. Ruò	A. Sūn		E. Xiōng	C. Áo
B. Zhǐ	#36.	F. Liú	D. Yuè	B. Mài	#111.	F. Gōng	D. Chú
C. Pín	A. Gòng		E. Xīng	C. Guó	A. Táng		E. Yùn
D. Quán	B. Kuàng	#55.	F. Tóng	D. Hú	B. Hú	#130.	F. Zì
E. Zhù	C. Chù	A. Tóu		E. Tí	C. Wēi	A. Kuài	
F. Zhòu	D. Chè	B. Zhú	#74.	F. Huán	D. Wén	B. Tùn	#149.
	E. Diǎo	C. Fǔ	A. Kè		E. Mù	C. Jùn	A. Shēn
#18.	F. Tiáo	D. Pǐ	B. Kǒng	#93.	F. Xiàn	D. Yàn	B. Jiǒng
A. Hù		E. Jǔ	C. Tāng	A. Bāo		E. Lā	C. Lóng
B. Yāng	#37.	F. Xī	D. Jiá	B. Yì	#112.	F. Jiāng	D. Zhì
C. Fèn	A. Jiào		E. Dùn	C. Shì	A. Zhàng		E. Cāng
D. Kē	B. Kǒng	#56.	F. Sān	D. Rán	B. Zhóu	#131.	F. Bǎn
E. Jǐng	C. Tè	A. Xù		E. Xiá	C. Bó	A. Gāo	
F. Xián	D. Sī	B. Jīn	#75.	F. Xiá	D. Jìn	B. Nèi	#150.
	E. Wǎn	C. Diàn	A. Kuǎn		E. Yú	C. Guǎn	A. Yǐng
#19.	F. Chī	D. Zàng	B. Zhì	#94.	F. Hán	D. Qián	B. Chéng
A. Jiōng		E. Hōng	C. Chóu	A. Qù		E. Fù	C. Cǎi
B. Yuè	#38.	F. Zhā	D. Qián	B. Xū	#113.	F. Jùn	D. Hú
C. Zhōu	A. Cǎi		E. Ér	C. Qìn	A. Liǎn		E. Hǎi
D. Sù	B. Táng	#57.	F. Pín	D. Lēi	B. Tóng	#132.	F. Háo
E. Yì	C. Tí	A. Chēn		E. Jiāo	C. Cú	A. Nǎi	

Milton Keynes UK
Ingram Content Group UK Ltd.
UKHW050641221123
432980UK00014B/782